TWELVE KEYS TO AN EFFECTIVE CHURCH

The Study Guide

KENNON L. CALLAHAN
and
IAN B. TANNER

HarperSanFrancisco
A Division of HarperCollinsPublishers

The National Institute for Church Planning and Consultation, of which Kennon L. Callahan is the founder and senior consultant, can be addressed at 15775 Hillcrest #455, Dallas TX 75248.

FIRST HARPERCOLLINS EDITION PUBLISHED IN 1992.

Library of Congress Catalog Card Number: 91–55475
ISBN 0–06–061305–X

92 93 94 95 96 ❖ MAL 10 9 8 7 6 5 4 3 2 1

Grace and Peace

To our many friends in

> the United States of America
>
> Australia
>
> New Zealand
>
> Canada
>
> Korea
>
> Central and South America
>
> England
>
> Africa
>
> and across the planet

who are using the Twelve Keys principles to grow forward the mission of countless congregations.

God's grace is amazing.

The welcome that the Twelve Keys principles have received has been deep, full, and generous. The friendships we now share are extraordinary. It is like discovering new family. We are blessed with countless friends all across the planet.

Our prayers are with you. May a genuine spirit of compassion and a deep sense of community be yours.

Know that God's grace and peace always surround you. God leads you forward.

Kennon and Julie Callahan

Contents

Acknowledgments

In 1988, Julie and I made our first trip to Australia and New Zealand—to help congregations with their mission.

I am grateful to my longtime friend George Morris, who gave much encouragement for us to go. I had had some reluctance. My teaching, research, writing, and consultation practice on this continent are extensive and fulfilling.

As of this writing, we have completed four major trips—1988, 1989, 1990, and 1991. We are most grateful for our many friendships all across Australia and New Zealand.

What we have learned has surpassed what we have shared. The wisdom and insights shared with us have deepened our compassion and given us a fuller sense of God's mission.

Good friends are the rich treasures of this life. On our first trip, we came to know Ian Tanner. His wisdom and wit, insight and integrity, compassion for persons and love for the Church's mission are compelling.

In 1990, after our second trip, Ian wrote a Lenten Study Guide for *Twelve Keys to an Effective Church*. It was used widely by congregations across South Australia. A multitude of requests for copies came from other parts of Australia and New Zealand. Together, Ian and I decided a further, revised edition would be useful. Final responsibility for this edition rests with me. Suggestions and new ideas are invited as your benefit from the *Study Guide*.

I want to thank Heather Bald, who has been invaluable in the initial development of the *Study Guide*. Her compassion, administrative competencies, and insights have strengthened the work greatly.

I want to thank John Shopp, senior editor at HarperSanFrancisco and Hilary Vartanian, senior editorial assistant, for their major contributions to the publication of this work.

I want to thank Julia McCoy Callahan for her suggestions and contributions. It is a rich experience to share and work together with her.

Kennon L. Callahan

February 1992

Introduction

MAJOR STEPS

Three steps advance your congregation's mission:

STUDY——PLAN——ACTION

These resources help with each step:

STUDY   *Twelve Keys to an Effective Church*, the basic text, and
        the *Twelve Keys Study Guide*

PLAN   *The Planning Workbook* and
        The Leaders' Guide, Part I

ACTION *Effective Church Leadership* and
        The Leaders' Guide, Parts II, III

Welcome to a great adventure!

Welcome to the first step—STUDY.

STEERING COMMITTEE

Many congregations find it helpful to develop a steering committee to facilitate the Study——Plan——Action steps.

The guidelines for developing this team are found in *The Leaders' Guide*, pages 57–64. This team gives leadership to the Study step.

PRINCIPLES FOR STUDY GROUPS

1. Set up the study groups so the maximum number of people can attend.
    Consistent with **the sixth key**, solid participatory decision making encourages
    every member of the church to share in the study.

2. Meet in a pleasant situation, with well-prepared and sensitive
    leadership, so group experience builds enthusiasm and develops
    an expectation for more.

3. Anticipate the Action step. Encourage group members to ask questions like:

    "Is this one of our strengths or weaknesses?"

    "What has to happen so that we can do better what we do well now?"

    "How does a newcomer to our church see us?"

    "How does this relate to my own life, and the life of my family?"

SETTING UP STUDY GROUPS

The object of the Study step is to discover the foundational principles, not to get
bogged down in "what to do." We encourage you to focus on action objectives later
in the Planning step. The steering committee will know best how to arrange the
Study.

1. A CONGREGATION STUDY

    Set aside a particular period, such as Lent, Ascension to Pentecost, or Advent,
    as a designated time for Sunday School classes and home study groups to
    study *Twelve Keys*.

2. RETREAT STUDY GROUPS

    Small groups studies are most helpful in a relaxed retreat setting. Many
    churches do their study in a weekend retreat.

3. BRIEF STUDIES AT NORMAL MEETINGS

    Studies can be shared on the normal agendas of Elders, Councils, Fellowship
    Groups, Youth Groups, etc.

4. SHUT-INS/ELDERLY MEMBERS STUDY

    Members unable to attend the study groups also have a concern for their
    church. Circulate, say, ten copies of *Twelve Keys* among shut-ins and elderly
    members each week. Audio tapes of *Twelve Keys* are available and can be
    circulated weekly.

THE STUDY GUIDE

Each study in the *Study Guide* concentrates on one central characteristic of effective churches. Each study is organized as follows:

Opening quotations to encourage reflection and prayer

Introducing this central characteristic

Looking at the Bible

Unlocking the key

A closing quotation to encourage reflection and prayer

The Twelve Keys principles are helpful with your church, work, family, and life.

Study them prayerfully—with anticipation. Your life will count fully and richly for God's mission!

LEADING STUDY GROUPS

Each study will be a rich time of worship, fellowship, and learning. We offer a few practical pointers.

1. Make sure invitations to participants are warm, enthusiastic, and personal.

2. Give as much notice as you can. Make sure group members know the study schedule well in advance, the location of the group, and starting and finishing times.

3. Ensure that all group members have read the appropriate chapter of *Twelve Keys to an Effective Church* prior to the study. Most will want their own copy. Others may read a circulating copy. Please do not photocopy chapters of the book for distribution.

4. Begin each study session with worship, singing if appropriate, some personal sharing, and prayers. Conclude with prayer and a benediction. Refreshments are on option for each group, but allow plenty of time for the study period.

5. Note that there are twelve chapters, not including the two introductory sections and the conclusion. Each of the twelve chapters can be studied in about forty-five minutes. The first six keys may require slightly more time.

   If possible, plan for twelve study sessions. Some groups decide on eight study sessions.

   If the group decides to meet on six occasions, study one chapter from the first six keys (1–6) and one chapter from the second six keys (7–12) on each occasion.

6. We suggest you not begin your study with the first key. Begin with something with which the group feels more familiar, such as Key 2, *pastoral and lay visitation*, or Key 3, *corporate, dynamic worship*.

7. Surround all the long-range planning events with continual prayer.
   Our real task is not to construct the picture we want, but to discern the future God has both promised and prepared for His Church in mission. That invites our best prayer.

—*Kennon L. Callahan*

STUDY 1

SPECIFIC CONCRETE MISSIONAL OBJECTIVES

The Church exists for mission as a fire exists for burning.
—Emil Brunner

INTRODUCING "SPECIFIC CONCRETE MISSIONAL OBJECTIVES"

It is very significant that *Specific Concrete Missional Objectives* is the first priority in *Twelve Keys to an Effective Church*.

The word *mission* means *to be sent out. Mission, missions, missionary,* all stem from the same idea of being sent out with a task to be accomplished. The very word *mission* reminds us that the gospel is not something we can keep to ourselves. We are always under Christ's invitation to take it out from the center of our church and share it with others. A congregation which is self-interested and turns in on itself has no sense of mission. It is not fully a Christian congregation.

Specific means that the local congregation has focused its mission on particular hurts and hopes in the community. Some members are called by God to offer help and hope to people who are suffering particular hurts, e.g., alcoholism, poverty, homelessness. These are specific. The congregation will be partners with the wider Church in supporting national and overseas mission projects. And, it is equally important that the congregation share in its local area as a people of compassion in practical, unselfish mission with others.

Concrete means practical help actually given, not just planned or publicized. Planning, research, prayer, and publicity may well precede the mission, but it is not concrete until action is begun. Jesus calls us to very concrete tasks—*feed the hungry, clothe the naked, visit the prisoner, heal the sick.* (Matt. 25:34–40).

The term *missional* includes help both to individuals in their need and to the social conditions which caused the need. For example, a congregation may be concerned at the exploitation of older persons in private nursing homes. It also should look at the legislation governing the management of such homes, and seek to prevent further exploitation.

Objectives means that the missional tasks are stated in such a way that the people undertaking them will know when they have been achieved. When the objectives are clear it will then be possible to evaluate the ongoing effectiveness of the congregation's mission.

Refer to pages 1 and 2 of **Twelve Keys to an Effective Church,** *and check your understanding of these important definitions. Can you illustrate them further?*

LOOKING AT THE BIBLE

LUKE 7:18–23

John's disciples told him about all these things. Calling two of them, he sent them to the Lord to ask, "Are you the one who was to come, or should we expect someone else?"

When the men came to Jesus, they said, "John the Baptist sent us to you to ask, Are you the one who was to come, or should we expect someone else?"

At that very time Jesus cured many who had diseases, sicknesses and evil spirits, and gave sight to many who were blind. So he replied to the messengers, "Go back and report to John what you have seen and heard: The blind receive sight, the lame walk, those who have leprosy are cured, the deaf hear, the dead are raised, and the good news is preached to the poor. Blessed is the man who does not fall away on account of me."

John the Baptist's message was the promise of the imminent coming of the Messiah or Christ. He had proclaimed the coming of the Lord in terms of the Old Testament expectations of a conquering King. He had realized the uniqueness of Jesus whom he had baptised, but Jesus didn't quite fit the ancient stereotype. John was now Herod's prisoner in the dungeons of the Castle of Machaerus. He knew he didn't have long to live. He wanted to know if Jesus really was the Messiah.

Verse 20: **When the men came to Jesus.** The congregation advertises itself as the representative of God, the body of the Christ. People have a right to come to a congregation and ask, *Are you really God's servants, or should we look elsewhere?*

How would you answer this question on behalf of your congregation?

Verse 21: **At that very time Jesus cured many.** Notice the immediate proof Jesus offered. At that very time Jesus demonstrated his power of love and healing. He didn't say, *look what I did last year*, or *fifty years ago our forebears did a great work here*, or *I will someday do a great work*. The evidence was there for all to see **at that very time**.

Is there sufficient evidence to persuade enquirers that God is in the midst of your congregation now?

Verse 22: **The blind receive sight, the lame walk, those who have leprosy are cured, the deaf hear, the dead are raised, and the good news is preached to the poor.**

This is quite specific, concrete mission with clear objectives and the proof is overwhelmingly conclusive.

What are the specific concrete human hurts and hopes in your immediate community which are calling out for help?

Are there two or three other people in your congregation who have the same concern as you do about a specific human hurt or hope in the community?

UNLOCKING THE FIRST KEY

1.   The 5 M's of the Christian church are discussed on pages 2–3.

   Discuss the implications of these for your church.

2.   On page 3, the statement is made: "In the eyes of God no person is unacceptable."

   Reflect with the group on the meaning of this statement in your own life and family.

3.   Three factors help in "growing mission up" (pages 4–6). When these three factors converge, the lives of many persons are touched with that specific, concrete mission.

   Share with the group one illustration where these three factors have converged in some congregation that has become a "living legend of help" (pages 8–9).

4.   Five invitational questions help persons to discover the mission to which God is calling them (pages 6–8).

   Share with the group your own current answers to these invitational questions.

*So long as the Church seeks to be the center of people's lives it is no different from the other entities of our culture that clamor to gain the central place in people's lives. When the Church decides to be **in** the center of people's lives, the Church transcends the entities of the culture; it gives up its own self-seeking, survival-oriented tendencies and becomes an entity focused on compassion, on serving, sharing, and caring. Whenever the Church does this the Church is truly the Church.*

—Kennon L. Callahan

STUDY 2

PASTORAL
AND LAY VISITATION

It is evident that many people are in desperate need. People today in their work, in their marriage and family, in the single state, in the many forms of social life in which they move, in their scientific work, in their leisure hours often feel themselves at the mercy of forces from within and without themselves, which they can barely cope with, if indeed they are not completely overwhelmed.

In this situation it is of immense importance that the irreplaceable significance of the pastoral conversation shall again be recognised as a commandment of the Lord and a blessing for innumerable people.

—Heije Faber

INTRODUCING "PASTORAL AND LAY VISITATION"

Nobody will be surprised to discover that visiting is high on the list of keys to an effective church. Visiting is central to the experience of Christianity. God himself is a visitor. "Praise to the Lord, the God of Israel for he has visited and redeemed his people." (Luke 1:68).

J.B. Phillips once wrote a play about "The Visited Planet." The coming of Christ is the greatest visit of all. Visiting is the key by which many people will come into dialogue with God and find meaning and hope for their lives.

There is a desperate need for pastoral and lay visitation. While we often use the term *pastoral* in the general sense of Christian caring, here it is used in the sense of the care offered by the *pastor,* that is, the ordained minister. Ministers are encouraged to visit widely in their parish. This personal contact of the minister with people is *shepherding,* which, of course, is also related to the pastoral images.

Many ministers say they find visiting in the parish time-consuming and, except for emergencies, relatively unproductive. They give it a low priority. How important does the group think the visiting of the minister is to church members and to the "unchurched" in our community?

There is also a desperate need for lay visitation. In one denomination the Council of Elders is required to *visit regularly members and adherents.* But no mention is made of elders visiting people outside the church. Note well, *whenever the focus of visitation is (only) within the church, one the major sources of outreach in the community is lost (page 11).*

For visiting to be most effective it should be shared between ministers and lay leaders. The visiting should be equally divided between church families, those in hospitals or homebound, and the unchurched families in the communitiy.

Has your congregation made a mistake in asking elders only to visit the members and adherents? Who should do the visitation to the unchurched community?

LOOKING AT THE BIBLE

ACTS 9:10–19

In Damascus there was a disciple named Ananias. The Lord called to him in a vision, "Ananias!". "Yes, Lord," he answered. The Lord told him, "Go to the house of Judas on Straight Street and ask for a man from Tarsus named Saul, for he is praying. In a vision he has seen a man named Ananias come and place his hands on him to restore his sight."

"Lord," Ananias answered, "I have heard many reports about this man and all the harm he has done to your saints in Jerusalem. And he has come here with authority from the chief priests to arrest all who call on your name."

But the Lord said to Ananias, "Go! This man is my chosen instrument to carry my name before the Gentiles and their kings and before the people of Israel. I will show him how much he must suffer for my name."

Then Ananias went to the house and entered it. Placing his hands on Saul, he said, "Brother Saul, the Lord—Jesus, who appeared to you on the road as you were coming here—has sent me so that you may see again and be filled with the Holy Spirit." Immediately, something like scales fell from Saul's eyes, and he could see again. He got up and was baptised, and after taking some food, he regained his strength."

This passage immediately follows the record of the conversion of Saul (Paul) on the road to Damascus. It tells of the visit of Ananias to Paul. We never hear of Ananias again, yet the visit of Ananias to Paul was crucial for Paul's acceptance as a Christian and the beginning of his ministry as the great apostle to the Gentiles.

Verses 11, 12: Notice that the visit of Ananias was a response to the Lord's command. All pastoral visiting is done in the knowledge that the visitor is one who is sent by the Lord (mission again!).

Verses 13, 14: **I have heard many reports about this man.** Notice that Paul was regarded by Ananias as a most unlikely prospect. In Ananias' view the possibility of this person becoming a Christian was zero. We need to remember that behind anonymous and unlikely doors in every street there are potential disciples of the Lord waiting to be invited by us to their life mission.

Verses 15, 16: Ananias spoke honestly to the Lord before he began his visiting. All effective visiting takes place in the context of sincere and honest prayer. It's all right to tell the Lord you don't want to go and you're scared! Then go.

Verse 17: **Brother Saul.** Ananias addressed Paul as *brother.* Although he had never met this unknown stranger before, he knew he must regard him as a brother. This attitude of acceptance and anticipated friendship without conditions is an essential key to Christian visitation.

Verse 18, 19: The visit of Ananias to Paul was a great blessing to both of them. Paul experienced salvation in body, mind, and spirit.

What blessing do you think Ananias received?

Our visiting may not lead to such dramatic consequences, but a visit made in love and the Holy Spirit is never lost. Notice Ananias made no demand on Paul. He didn't require repentance or a promise of better behavior, or suggest he should go to church.

Ananias only had one item on his agenda. What was it? Translate it into a contemporary sentence that would communicate clearly to unchurched families in your community when you knock on their door and they ask what you want.

UNLOCKING THE SECOND KEY

1. On page 11, a visiting schedule is suggested for a congregation with an average worship attendance of two hundred people.

    Adjusting the figures for the size of your own congregation, how does the number of visits (as far as you know them) match this standard?

2. It is helpful to think of visitation in four major stages: selecting and seeking; sharing and shepherding; relating and reaching; winning and working.

    Ask a member of the group to comment on the definition of these pairs of words (pages 15, 16). How can these stages be incorporated in a visiting mission in your congregation?

3. On pages 20–21, the Ten Foundational Principles on the Art of Effective Visitation are set out. List these ten principles in summary form (i.e., three or four words per principle) on a sheet of newsprint or poster-card. **Discuss them as a group.**

    Pre-invite two or three people to prepare a role-play of a "normal" visit illustrating some or all of these principles. As a variation, several pairs or trios may volunteer to illustrate one or two of the principles each.

4. All the members of the group have been visiting for the church in some form or another.

    Ask what new thought or ideas this key of pastoral and lay visitation has stirred in you.

The purpose of pastoral and lay visitation is not to hustle people into the neat and nifty programs and activities of a local church. The purpose of pastoral and lay visitation is a deeper, more profound discovery of central and common relationships among fellow travelers through this life's journey.

—Kennon L. Callahan

STUDY 3

CORPORATE, DYNAMIC WORSHIP

Worship is the nourishment of the mind upon the truth of God,
It is the arousing of the conscience by the holiness of God,
It is the cleansing of the imagination by the holiness of God;
It is the enlargement of the heart by the love of God
It is the offering of ourselves in the service of God.
                                        —*William Temple (adapted)*

INTRODUCING "CORPORATE, DYNAMIC WORSHIP"

Worship is a word that comes from two English words, *worth ship. Worship* means to express the **worth** of a person or thing. Sometimes important people like judges or magistrates or civic leaders are addressed as *Your Worship.* It simply means they are persons of worth.

Divine worship is the expression of our sense of the worth of God. Remember that *while we were yet sinners Christ died for us* (Romans 5:8). That is how God expressed our worth to him. We can do no less than that. A Christian definition of worship can be no less than the offering of the whole of our life in the service of God. A service of worship then is sacramental; it signifies what the whole of our life is meant to be like.

The forms by which we offer a service of worship to God (the liturgy) is the gift to the Church of centuries of tradition and experience. We constantly review and renew our service of worship to make sure it assists the worshipers to know the presence of God with them in the best possible way, and to respond with the deepest compassion.

The two adjectives which characterize this sort of worship are *corporate* and *dynamic.*

Corporate means *whenever there is a strong sense of belonging, a strong sense of togetherness and community amongst the people who share in it* (page 24).

Dynamic means *whenever the service stirs and inspires the people who participate in it and whenever profound help and hope are shared with and among them* (page 24).

What do the two adjectives chosen to describe inspiring worship mean to you?

LOOKING AT THE BIBLE

> ## ROMANS 12:1–2
> Therefore, I urge you, brothers, in view of God's mercy, to offer your bodies as living sacrifices, holy and pleasing to God—which is your spiritual worship. Do not conform any longer to the pattern of this world, but be transformed by the renewing of your mind. Then you will be able to test and approve what God's will is—his good, pleasing and perfect will.

The letter to the Romans was written by Paul near the end of his ministry, and is the most comprehensive and profound of all his writing. The first eleven chapters of Romans deals with Paul's understanding of God's plan for his creation, and the centrality of Christ as Savior and Lord. The twelfth chapter is a change of gear! Here Paul begins to apply his teaching to the practical implications in the Christian's life. That's why it begins with the word **therefore**.

Verse 1: We are **urged**, not commanded, to worship God. Worship is a free response to God. **In view of God's mercy** means that the basis of the appeal is God's love for us demonstrated in his dying for us so we might have life. **God's mercy** has been the subject of the first eleven chapters.

Offer your bodies means the offer of the total person—body, mind and spirit. **Living sacrifices** is consistent with the theme of the New Testament. Christ came that we might have life. The Old Testament was concerned with **dead** sacrifices. God wants us to live in his service. **Holy and pleasing to God** are the words used to describe sacrifices acceptable in the Old Testament. **Spiritual worship** is sincere worship offered by mind and heart. Compare John 4:24, *worshipers must worship in spirit and in truth.*

Verse 2: **Do not conform any longer to the pattern of this world.** True worship can only be offered when we are true people. We may therefore need to change—to be transformed inwardly. How is this to happen? By **the renewing of our minds.** How are our minds to be renewed? By living with the Spirit. The shorthand term is *the means of grace*—mission, Bible, worship, prayer, sacraments, the influence of a congregation, and practical service all contribute to the renewing of the mind. Then we experience the giving of our whole person, wholly offered to God, in the unity of the congregation, for the whole of our life.

What is the relationship between what we do on Sunday in a service of worship, and what we do in the other 167 hours of the week? Do your present services of worship really have an effect on the practical behavior of the worshipers who attend your congregation during the rest of the week?

UNLOCKING THE THIRD KEY

1. Five characteristics describe corporate, dynamic worship:

    the warmth and winsomeness of the service and the congregation (pages 24–27)

    the dynamic and inspiration of the music (pages 27–28)

    the character and quality of the preaching (pages 28–29)

    the power and movement of the liturgy (page 29)

    the seating range of the sanctuary (pages 29–31)

    Reflect on each of these characteristics in relation to your own congregation. Which one or two are current strengths? Which one or two make best sense for your congregation to improve now?

2. Under the heading of "Development Possibilities" (pages 31–32), three areas are suggested for a congregation to work on. The first relates to the pastor. The second highlights the importance of music. The third relates to worship attendance, membership growth, and income.

    What can your congregation do about these three developmental possibilities?

3. The chapter is summed up this way:

    Worship will continue in the foreseeable future to be one of the major places where unchurched persons and newcomers come to discover whether a congregation will share with them help and hope in strong, warm and winsome ways. (page 33)

    What is your reflection on this statement?

*As you develop your long-range plan, plan to celebrate worship on the **first day** of the week. If you think your week begins on Monday morning in the office or at your job, your worship is occurring on the last day of the week. Some pastors make the mistake of thinking their work week begins on Monday morning in the office rather than on Sunday in worship with the congregation. Whenever a pastor (or member) sees his or her work week beginning with worship on the first day of the week, there will be a sense of expectancy, vision, and hope in that church.*

—Kennon L. Callahan

STUDY 4

SIGNIFICANT RELATIONAL GROUPS

*Christianity means community through Jesus Christ and in Jesus Christ.
No Christian community is more or less than this. Whether it be a brief,
single encounter or the daily fellowship of years, Christian community is
only this. We belong to one another only through and in Jesus Christ.*
                                                    —*Dietrich Bonhoeffer*

INTRODUCING
"SIGNIFICANT RELATIONAL GROUPS"

A congregation is more than an assembly of individuals who meet together for
worship each Sunday. We are like a family where the care and love for one another
continues through the whole week. The closeness of the compassion and community between members of the congregation is the chief witness to the reality of the
presence of the Holy Spirit in the midst of the Church.

One can be mutually caring for large numbers of people by helping every member
relate to a small group within the larger congregation.

A "group" can vary from three or four persons to thirty or forty persons. The emphasis is on the **relational** character of the group. **Relational** groups are character-
ized by the qualities of caring and sharing between members of the group. People
discover a sense of roots, place, and belonging.

Groups in the church can have wide and varied purposes, such as Bible study,
prayer, youth, missions, and committee functions. The tasks of the various groups in
the church may vary but the fact is that in a *significant relational group* people matter
more than programs, and broken hearts and human hopes have a higher priority
than the "tasks" of the group.

LOOKING AT THE BIBLE

ACTS 2:42–47

They devoted themselves to the apostles' teaching and to the fellowship, to the breaking of bread and to prayer. Everyone was filled with awe, and many wonders and miraculous signs were done by the apostles. All the believers were together and had everything in common. Selling their possessions and goods, they gave to anyone as he had need. Every day they continued to meet together in the temple courts. They broke bread in their homes and ate together with glad and sincere hearts, praising God and enjoying the favour of all the people. And the Lord added to their number daily those who were being saved.

This is the first description of the Christian congregation established in Jerusalem.

Verse 42: **The apostles' teaching and fellowship.** Notice how the teaching ministry is not delivered as an academic lecture, but associated in the context of warm fellowship. **The breaking of bread** may have been the Eucharist, or the continuation of the Jewish custom of an enacted grace. There is no doubt it invoked the memory of Jesus' words *"Take, eat, this is my body broken for you.'*

Verse 43: **Filled with awe**—a sense of something momentous happening around them. Does that describe your congregation? **Many wonders and miraculous signs**—visible signs of the presence of God were evident.

Verse 46: **They continued to meet together** with their fellow Jews for the set times of prayer in the temple courts. They didn't isolate themselves from the rest of the community.

This congregation had grown to three thousand and was continuing to grow every day. The intense caring and sharing described here could not have been sustained in such a large assembly, so **they broke bread in their homes. . . .** Jewish people had a long tradition of home worship, but this was the beginning of the house-church movement. With these "significant relational groups" the growth of the Jerusalem Church was sustained.

Identify in contemporary Church terms the characteristics of this New Testament congregation.

UNLOCKING THE FOURTH KEY

1. There are four sections in this chapter: Community, Not Committees; New People and New Groups; Caring and Sharing; People, Not Programs.

    In advance invite members of your group each to prepare a summary of one section, and relate it to "our" congregation. Other members of the group may comment at the conclusion of each presentation.

2. On page 35, the search for community has been identified as one of the four major life searches.

    How does your congregation help you to fulfill this foundational life search?

3. In the section New People and New Groups (pages 36, 37), a number of insights are shared related to new groupings.

    What new groupings has your congregation started in the last five years? What new groupings will be helpful to start in the coming five years?

Many, many unchurched persons are attracted to churches that communicate and share a sense of compassion and community. What draws people to a church is their search for community—roots, place, belonging.

—Kennon L. Callahan.

NOTES

STUDY 5

STRONG LEADERSHIP RESOURCES

To rise from a zero to be a great hero,
To answer three questions you'll strive.
Where are we going?
How will we get there?
And how will we know we've arrived?
　　　　　　　　　　—Anonymous

INTRODUCING
"STRONG LEADERSHIP RESOURCES"

It is important to notice how this fifth key is titled. It could have been called *Strong, Resourceful Leaders.* Instead this essential characteristic is identified as strong leadership *resources.* The implication is that every member of the congregation can be helped to exercise leadership. The primary task of a leader in the Church is to facilitate leadership in others. Hence the need is to speak of leadership *resources.*

At the same time, leadership is more than the role of only being an enabler in getting other people to lead. *Leaders are those who effectively lead* (page 41).

What do you think is a reasonable description of the tasks of leadership in your congregation?

LOOKING AT THE BIBLE

EPHESIANS 4:7; 4:11–13

But to each one of us grace has been given as Christ apportioned it.

It was [Christ] who gave some to be apostles, some to be prophets, some to be evangelists, and some to be pastors and teachers, to prepare God's people for works of service, so that the body of Christ may be built up until we all reach unity in the faith and in the knowledge of the Son of God and become mature, attaining to the whole measure of the fullness of Christ.

In the first three chapters of Ephesians, Paul develops his understanding of how God will make known his plan for the whole world through the Church (Ephesians 3:10). In this fourth chapter Paul goes on to teach about the quality of the Church and its leadership so that it may fulfill this enormous responsibility.

Verse 7: God in Christ gives people gifts. For a church to refuse to recognize the gifts in its members, or be careless in employing them in mission, is to deny God. God's gifts to the Church are not primarily buildings or money but gifted people whom he has called into the congregation.

Verse 11: There is a diversity of gifts and abilities in any congregation. Leaders are never the same.

God gave us different gifts **as Christ apportioned it.** There is no need for envy in the church—just gratitude that others can do well.

Notice that this verse identifies the leadership tasks necessary in the Ephesian Church. You will note that each list of leaders in the New Testament (e.g. Romans 12:6–8; I Corinthians 12:28–30; I Timothy 3) is different. The gifts of leadership needed are different for different contexts.

Verse 12: The leaders' task is not to **do** the work of ministry, but to lead all the members in their work of mission **service so that the body of Christ may be built up** through the increasing participation of more persons in God's mission. God gives to each Christian the gifts necessary for their share in the mission. We are all at different stages of development in the use of our gifts.

Verse 13: Leadership in the Church is corporate. The only singular leader is Christ. The rest of us are a team. The leadership **team** in any church involves every member of the congregation growing together in the unity of our diversity to **the fullness of Christ.**

Share with the group a recent time when you have experienced this sense of a leadership team.

UNLOCKING THE FIFTH KEY

1. Ask the group to list on newsprint the points made under the eight headings of *Leaders and Achievements* (pages 41–45).

    How would the group envisage these principles being put into practice in your own congregation?

2. Under the heading of *Mission and Leaders* (pages 45–46), it is suggested that the local congregation deploy fifty percent of its leaders serving the community outside the church.

    How many of your congregation's leaders work is "inside-the-church-walls" and how many are invested in mission and service to those outside? What approximately are the percentages?

3. In the section *The Pastor and the Staff* (pages 48–53), six principles for strong pastoral and staff leadership are shared.

    Which four of these principles will be most helpful in your congregation now?

Churches with a strong track record of action, implementation, and momentum do not focus on getting people to fill slots where the church needs a body. Instead these churches focus on helping people to discover where their specific gifts and competencies can best be shared.

                                                        —*Kennon L. Callahan*

NOTES

STUDY 6

STREAMLINED STRUCTURE AND SOLID PARTICIPATORY DECISION MAKING

Renewal, after all, is about builders. Many people can introduce change for change's sake and call it renewal. That is illusory. A builder, on the other hand, leads an organization toward renewal that outlives the presence of any single individual and revitalizes even as it changes.

Go for simplicity in what is admittedly a complex world.
— *Robert H. Waterman, Jr.*

INTRODUCING "STREAMLINED STRUCTURE AND SOLID PARTICIPATORY DECISION MAKING"

The structure of a church flows from its own understanding of its mission. Structure is a servant of mission. The *planners* of any structure best begin their task by first discovering the missional *nature* of the church, then its *functions* and finally its *order* or structure.

Review the structures and processes that govern your congregation's life. Can we "streamline" the local structures within our congregation? How? (See pages 59, 60).

Also review your decision-making processes. *Solid* decisions result from an input of wisdom, a sense of priorities, and character. *Participatory* means that the formal process of making the decision is preceded by wide, frank, and informal discussion among all members. No attempt should be made to withhold information or be secretive. The decision should be made in a way so that it is possible for the majority to know that the decision is theirs, and they are willing to *own* it.

Do **solid** *and* **participatory** *describe the decision-making process of your church? If not, what adjectives do?*

LOOKING AT THE BIBLE

ACTS 15:24–29

We have heard that some went out from us without our authorization and disturbed you, troubling your minds by what they said. So we all agreed to choose some men and send them to you with our dear friends Barnabas and Paul—men who have risked their lives for the name of our Lord Jesus Christ. Therefore we are sending Judas and Silas to confirm by word of mouth what we are writing. It seemed good to the Holy Spirit and to us not to burden you with anything beyond the following requirements. You are to abstain from food sacrificed to idols, from blood, from the meat of strangled animals and from sexual immorality. You will do well to avoid these things.

The first part of Acts 15 is the minutes of the first meeting of the national Council of the Christian Church. Some of the enthusiastic Jewish Christians had been teaching the Gentile (non-Jewish) converts that they had to be circumcised before they could become Christians and claim Christ's salvation. That is, they had to become Jews before becoming Christians.

The Council, consisting of the Apostles and the Elders of the Church, met in Jerusalem to decide this question. The text of Acts 15 discloses the decision-making process. Verses 2–21 sets out the sequence of events.

The verses we study are the text of the pastoral letter that was sent to the Gentile churches by the Council. The particular recommendations need not attract our attention at the moment. It is instructive to notice how they reported the decision-making process.

Verse 24: It began with the collection of reliable information regarding the crisis in the church.

Verses 25, 26: The conveying of the decision was not only by letter but also by four representatives of great stature in the church to explain and commend the decision. This was the "follow-through" mechanism. The decision-making process is beautifully described by the phrase **it seemed good to the Holy Spirit and to us.**

Within the agreed processes of your congregation's decision making, what has to be done so that you can say with conviction when you make a decision: "it seemed good to the Holy Spirit and to us"?

UNLOCKING THE SIXTH KEY

1. On pages 59–60, three principles of a streamlined organizational structure are shared.

    Which two of the three will best benefit your congregation now?

2. On page 60, a section called *Effective Decisions* begins. The group can reflect on a major decision taken by the congregation within the memory of the people present.

    Did the decision-making process live out these suggestions? Where could it have been better handled? Concentrate on the process, and not the issue which was decided!

3. *Follow-through* is as important as the decision. There are many decisions in the minutes of church committees which have never been implemented because no follow-through was agreed.

    Can the group illustrate good follow-through in a recent meeting held in the congregation?

*Long-range planning invites the best **mutual** wisdom, judgment, vision, common sense and prayer of all the participants.*

—*Kennon L. Callahan*

NOTES

STUDY 7

SEVERAL COMPETENT PROGRAMS AND ACTIVITIES

The devil has a device called "busyness" by which he deceives Christians into thinking that they are doing the will of God.

—Meister Eckhart

INTRODUCING "SEVERAL COMPETENT PROGRAMS AND ACTIVITIES"

You will remember that the introductory chapter points out that the first six characteristics of an effective church are relational and increase the satisfaction of the members; the second six are functional and primarily reduce dissatisfaction. We need to have this clearly in mind as we consider this key (see pages xiv, xv).

It is important to note that a congregation does not need all twelve keys in place. We will function well with five relational keys and four functional keys.

The monthly newsletter's listing of a congregation's programs and activities may look impressive, but does not guarantee the congregation's effectiveness in Christian mission. Busy congregations may be just that—busy!

Programs and activities are best qualified by the adjectives *several* and *competent*. *Several* doesn't mean trying to do everything every other church is doing. It means concentrating on a few programs the congregation can do well. While we may hope to give members a large menu of activities, we may in fact be heaping upon them too much work and pressure.

It is decisive that the programs of the church be *competent*. They should be done at least as competently as any secular organization. We must not accept lower standards because we are the church. Quite the reverse! In all our church programs and activities the care of people must come first. This is not a contradiction of the previous principle. Part of the care of people is to encourage them to delight in excellence.

If we are a busy church, this chapter deserves careful study.

LOOKING AT THE BIBLE

LUKE 10:38–42

As Jesus and his disciples were on their way, he came to a village where a woman named Martha opened her home to him. She had a sister called Mary, who sat at the Lord's feet listening to what he said. But Martha was distracted by all the preparations that had to be made. She came to him and asked, "Lord, don't you care that my sister has left me to do the work by myself? Tell her to help me!"

"Martha, Martha," the Lord answered, "you are worried and upset about many things, but only one thing is needed. Mary has chosen what is better, and it will not be taken away from her."

This incident in Jesus' life occurred as he was on his way to Jerusalem and the cross. In human terms his heart was full of foreboding and great tension. He needed a place of quiet and peace, and perhaps a listening ear which Mary offered. Martha was intent on involving him (and Mary) in "programs and activities."

Is your congregation a Mary congregation, or a Martha congregation?

Verse 39: **Listening to what he said**—another reminder of the importance of paying attention to Jesus. Compare Luke 9:35: **This is my Son, whom I have chosen; listen to him.** Perhaps this is also a reminder that in our human need even church leaders who seem to have it all together need the ministry of gracious listening. We all do!

Verse 40: **But Martha was distracted by all the preparations that had to be made.** Have you ever felt like that in the preparations for the church bazaar or other function?

Can church programs that reduce the leaders and helpers to irritable, fractious grumps really minister the grace of God to others?

Tell her to help me. Are our church activities genuinely designed to be of help to people, or do persons get a sense they've been invited to participate to increase the church's reputation?

Verse 41: You are worried and upset about many things.

Was Martha taking on too much? Are you?

Only one thing is needed.

What does the group think the one thing is? What change would happen in your congregation if this "one thing" were taken seriously?

UNLOCKING THE SEVENTH KEY

1. Ask various members of the group to give a summary of the various sections and propose an application to the congregation's present life.

2. "It takes four to five years to develop and build any program into a major program in the life of a church and a community" (page 68).

   Discuss whether your church has a program of that character and quality. Would it make sense for your congregation to develop this characteristic?

3. Ask members of the group:

   What is the most important message for our congregation at the present time in this chapter?

Sometimes we put on church glasses and only view those programs and activities that are directly a part of a church's work and mission. As a matter of fact, hope-fulfilling events and traumatic events that occur in the everyday lives of people in a congregation decisively affect and shape what is going on in that congregation.
                                                                    —*Kennon L. Callahan.*

NOTES

STUDY 8

OPEN ACCESSIBILITY

*We felt so welcome we couldn't **not** come back. Our family had intended to shop around for a church but found the welcome, the church service itself, and a call from the minister shortly after our first visit so inviting that we had to come back because St. John's had the sense of belongingness we were looking for.*

—Reported by Gordon Turner

INTRODUCING "OPEN ACCESSIBILITY"

This key is relevant to those congregations who meet in already established buildings. Most of us do not have much choice about location. Even congregations who are planning to build may discover that it is difficult to obtain the most desirable location.

Whatever your circumstances, it is a chapter worth studying. Church buildings and sites are not sacrosanct. Many congregations have rebuilt on more suitable sites when they have realized that their present location is an impediment to their mission.

Surrounding communities are never static. Many congregations previously on the edge of population centers have discovered they will soon be in the center of a new development. Long-range planning means asking questions about population and industry movements ten and twenty years down the track.

The question of accessibility is not only about physical location, but also accessibility to the building, and the accessibility of the congregational leaders. This study will have more relevance than you may think!

LOOKING AT THE BIBLE

MARK 2:1–5

A few days later, when Jesus again entered Capernaum, the people heard that he had come home. So many gathered that there was no room left, not even outside the door, and he preached the word to them. Some men came bringing to him a paralytic, carried by four of them. Since they could not get him to Jesus because of the crowd, they made an opening in the roof above Jesus and, after digging through it, lowered the mat the paralysed man was lying on. When Jesus saw their faith, he said to the paralytic, "Son, your sins are forgiven."

Here is a classic example of a church with severely limited accessibility!

Verse 1: **The people heard that he had come home.** If Jesus is truly in the Church the word will get around "the community grapevine." But we ought not to make it difficult for people to get to Jesus by bad planning or no planning.

Verse 2: **So many gathered that there was no room left, not even outside the door.** It's not often accessibility is blocked by too many worshipers, but it does happen. Sometimes worshipers create artificial blockages by blocking the ends of the pews and making it difficult for people to get past.

Does your congregation make access difficult for people who wish to attend? How? What about access for the disabled?

Verse 4: **Since they could not get him to Jesus because of the crowd.** Maybe there are other ways your congregation makes it difficult for people to get to Jesus, other than by physical barriers.

If a visitor in great need of Jesus' ministry came to your congregation, what would be the barriers he or she would discover that might prevent them experiencing that ministry?

Verse 5: **Your sins are forgiven.** Many people in our community are cursed with a debilitating sense of guilt or fear or anxiety. Some of them don't know there is a place where their sins may be forgiven. One of the congregation's prime tasks is to make it possible for people to come to Jesus.

Is this also an accessibility problem in your congregation? What have we done wrong that people in need don't make their way in droves to churches like ours to find forgiveness and new life?

UNLOCKING THE EIGHTH KEY

1. It's difficult for *insiders* to know how accessible their church is to *outsiders*. We really need to ask non-attenders how accessible our church building is.

    Ask an architect, or real-estate agent, or insurance surveyor to tell you what they think of your church's physical accessibility. Or take a tape recorder to the local shopping center and ask strangers whether they know where your church is and whether they would find it easy to visit!

2. A church unconsciously displays "hidden signs" (page 74).

    Go around the group and ask: What hidden signs do you think our congregation displays to visitors or passers-by?

3. Four ways of overcoming limited physical accessibility are suggested (pages 75, 76). What are they?

    If your Church building has inadequate physical accessibility, are there ways to overcome the problem?

4. You will have noticed that we have concluded each study with a quote from that chapter.

    What quote from this chapter would you put at the end of this study?

NOTES

STUDY 9

HIGH VISIBILITY

You have seen the house built, you have seen it adorned
By one who came in the night, it is now dedicated to GOD.
It is now a visible church, one more light set on a hill
In a world confused and dark and disturbed by portents of fear.
And what shall we say of the future? Is one church all we can build?
Or shall the Visible Church go on to conquer the World?
—T.S. Eliot

INTRODUCING "HIGH VISIBILITY"

Professor Marshall McLuhan coined the phrase "the medium is the message." He claimed that the actual medium of communication often tells a message louder than the message itself.

The central application of this principle for Christians is that the sort of person we are, and the sort of congregation we are, speaks louder than what we are trying to say.

Likewise, our church building is itself a message to those who pass by. Its architecture, its general appearance, the care we take of it, the attractiveness of its surroundings, the sign by which we identify it, all tell the passer-by or visitor something about our message.

This chapter is teaching us about the importance of the buildings we call "church." It is also reminding us of the grapevine effect of *human witness is word and action* in the local community, and alerting us to the possibilities of other important avenues of public witness—the media.

In our concern about reaching out to the *unchurched* this is a very important chapter for us to study.

LOOKING AT THE BIBLE

MATTHEW 5:14–16

You are the light of the world. A city on a hill cannot be hidden. Neither do people light a lamp and put it under a bowl. Instead they put it on its stand, and it gives light to everyone in the house. In the same way, let your light shine before men, that they may see your good deeds and praise your Father in heaven.

This passage is part of the Sermon on the Mount, and follows Jesus' teaching we call "The Beatitudes."

Verse 14: **You are the light of the world.** The Church of Jesus has the responsibility to be **a light to the nations.** Notice **light** is a collective noun—the community of Christians is to be the light. The Church is to continue Jesus' witness—*as long as I am in the world I am the light of the world* (John 9:5). **A city on a hill cannot be hidden.** Perhaps this refers to Jerusalem, clearly visible at night as well as by day. The obvious implication is that the Christian witness must not be hidden.

We are called to be the light of the world, not of the Church. The text in John 3:16 does not say, "For God so loved the Church." God's love is for the world. We are called to be the light of the world.

Verse 15: **It gives light to everyone in the house.** The house is the world. The light is to be light for the **world,** not the Church. The Church itself is to be the lamp, the source of light. Light from the lamp is the witness to the world. Compare Luke 8:16 *so that those who come in can see the light*—presumably a reference to the converted who saw the light and came to it.

Verse 16: **In the same way let your light shine.** Be visible!

They may see your good deeds—deeds, the primary form of the Christian message. The most visible and compelling witness of all. **And praise your Father in heaven**—the purpose of our visibility is not to draw attention to ourselves, but that many, many persons might praise God.

Could anyone in the group paraphrase these three verses in a way that will be a contemporary message for your own congregation?

UNLOCKING THE NINTH KEY

1. The eighth central characteristic is open accessibility. This chapter discusses
    the ninth central characteristic, namely, high visibility.

    *What do you understand to be the distinctions between accessibility and
    visibility?*

2. High visibility includes three components: physical visibility, community
    visibility, and media visibility.

    *Which of these does your congregation do well? Which two of these three
    components can you advance and improve?*

3. On pages 82–84 three areas are discussed: points of interest, signs, and people.

    *What can your church do to strengthen "points of interest"? What do persons
    in your community "see" when they look at your church's signs? Reflect on
    whether your congregation has a significant range of persons who are at work
    in the community helping people with their lives and destinies.*

*God has planted us on one of the richest mission fields on the planet. Just when
some of us had begun to think life was almost half over and all we had to do was
stay out of major trouble until the end, God has given us a new day. God calls us
to rethink the center and focus of our work and our lives.*

—*Kennon L. Callahan*

NOTES

STUDY 10

ADEQUATE PARKING, LAND, AND LANDSCAPING

We, too, the people of England,
Have built this Cathedral—men and women
Who know little of the making of beauty
But who, when beauty comes, can feel
Its presence—can find in their troubled lives
An anchorage, a haven, a calm assurance
Of something greater and beyond themselves
Which, though they die, survives.
—Clive Sanson

INTRODUCING "ADEQUATE PARKING, LAND, AND LANDSCAPING"

This key is relevant to city and rural congregations. The ability offered by the church to park a car on firm ground, securely, and in reasonable distance of the church building is a prime pre-accessibility factor anywhere.

In many recent surveys it is revealed, again and again, that the overwhelming majority of worship attenders travel to church by car. In many cases every person attending church arrived by car.

After a person's house, the next major capital investment is usually their car. Where the church shows care and respect for people's cars and for their safe and orderly parking, that congregation will be appreciated. In addition, of course, in our increasingly mobile society people will simply not attend a church if they have to walk three blocks or more. We may wish it was different, and recite how our granddad walked twenty miles to church and back every Sunday, but that was yesterday's reality. We have today's reality.

A newcomer who may decide to attend our congregation to see what we are like, and who cannot see safe and accessible parking, will just drive past!

The landscaping and garden environment of a church building is important to give a clear message to the passer-by. *The medium is the message again.*

What is the message your congregation is sharing? "No room in the Inn," or "Come on in, there's room in the Inn for you?"

LOOKING AT THE BIBLE

MARK 10:13–16

People were bringing little children to Jesus to have him touch them, but the disciples rebuked them. When Jesus saw this, he was indignant. He said to them, "Let the little children come to me, and do not hinder them, for the kingdom of God belongs to such as these. I tell you the truth, anyone who will not receive the kingdom of God like a little child will never enter it." And he took the children in his arms, put his hands on them and blessed them.

Parking facilitates people coming to Jesus. This passage reminds us that we are not to hinder anyone who wishes to come to Jesus and bring *the little ones* with them.

Verse 13: **Bringing little children to Jesus.** Technically the word for **children** means any child up to the age of twelve. No gospel text refers to "mothers" bringing the children. They could just as well be *fathers!* **Children** was sometimes used for the little ones—the physically or intellectually handicapped or disadvantaged.

But the disciples rebuked them. The disciples were not wicked men. They may have wanted to protect Jesus. Perhaps they saw he was tired. But it is a serious responsibility to decide to keep people away from Jesus.

Verse 14: **Jesus was indignant.**

In what ways do well-intentioned church leaders keep people away from Jesus' Church? Any experiences in your own congregation?

Do not hinder them. Hindering can be by fault, or default. That is, we can put physical or relational barriers in the way of people wanting to enter Jesus' Church, or we can be careless or unthinking about trying to make it easier for people to attend church.

What are some of the problems strangers or visitors face when they decide to attend your congregation? How could you make it easier from them?

UNLOCKING THE TENTH KEY

1. Complete the Church Parking Formula on page 88.

    What's the consequence for your congregation?

2. What percentage of your congregation comes to church by car? Since cars facilitate people's attendance at church, maybe we should pay more attention to them?

    What two or three objectives would help best?

3. On pages 92–93, *a winning combination* is discussed. Is your congregation *on a winner?*

    If not, what needs to be done?

If you want to worry, worry about something that counts. To worry about whether your local church will survive is to worry about a lesser thing. To worry for the human hurts and hopes of the many people who have yet to discover Christ—now that is a worry that counts!

—Kennon L. Callahan

NOTES

STUDY 11

ADEQUATE SPACE AND FACILITIES

And so we build buildings
Of towers and spires
Tall walls and stained glass windows;
With heavy doors and pews,
Beautiful buildings
Dedicated to God's work

Living things grow and change
And flower and bear fruit,
What of our church buildings?
—Ken Walsh

INTRODUCING "ADEQUATE SPACE AND FACILITIES"

A good place to begin is to read the last section of the chapter which is entitled *A house and a home*. Someone could read this section to the group (page 104).

The pattern of congregational buildings varies greatly for church life in the 1990s. Make allowance for alternative forms of congregational life, such as house churches. To be sure, the present evidence is that the majority of churchgoers attend a congregation meeting in a church building. However, the principles of adequate space and facilities apply to all forms of the Church, house churches, etc.

Make sure the capacity of your Sanctuary, Fellowship Hall, Sunday School and parking are in balance or else the capacity of the smallest unit will determine the size of your congregation.

Notice the principle that concludes the first section, *The Mistake of Underbuilding*. The principle is: *the buildings serve the mission*. Work through the long-range mission plan and consequent program of the congregation before committing the congregation to new building, or building extensions.

LOOKING AT THE BIBLE

REVELATION 21:10–16

And he carried me away in the Spirit to a mountain great and high, and showed me the Holy City, Jerusalem, coming down out of heaven from God. It shone with the glory of God, and its brilliance was like that of a very precious jewel, like a jasper, clear as crystal. It had a great, high wall with twelve gates, and with twelve angels at the gates. On the gates were written the names of the twelve tribes of Israel. There were three gates on the east, three on the north, three on the south and three on the west. The wall of the city had twelve foundations, and on them were the names of the twelve apostles of the Lamb. The angel who talked with me had a measuring rod of gold to measure the city, its gates and its wall. The city was laid out like a square, as long as it was wide. He measured the city with the rod and found it to be 12,000 stadia in length, and as wide and high as it is long.

The revelation of John is not an easy book to read, but this passage is not too difficult. It describes, in part, the Holy City, the new Jerusalem, the city of God, and therefore a vision in symbolic terms of the centerpiece of "heaven's real estate."

Verse 11: **It shone with the glory of God**—the city on the hill again, lit with the light of God. A **visible** church!

Verse 12: **It had a great high wall with twelve gates.** The high wall keeps out the enemies of God's people—the world, the flesh, and the devil. But the twelve gates suggest open accessibility. People from every point of the compass are welcome, and there will be no impediment to enter this community of God.

Verse 16: **He measured the city.** Each side of the city was about 1,500 miles long, and the total area of the city was 2,250,000 square miles! This is an unimaginable size for a city. John is clearly saying that in his vision of the city of God, there is plenty of room for everyone. God has provided adequate space!

In the buildings we build, we should always build in a way that lets everyone know they are most welcome. There is room for them.

What are the lessons here in this passage for your congregation?

UNLOCKING THE ELEVENTH KEY

This important chapter requires careful reading and analysis. Don't get too concerned with architectural calculations. They can wait for the planning stage. Concentrate on the main principles for now.

1. It could be helpful to have a floorplan of your church properties before the group. You could discuss the balance of the space available for each aspect of the congregation's present activities.

   With your best creativity, what would your group recommend for your church buildings?

2. In the section Building and Growing (pages 100–104), five principles are discussed.

   Which three of these will be most helpful to your congregation?

3. As a group, reflect on the quote below taken from the Leaders' Guide.

   Share your own sense of your life mission with the group.

We have loved our local churches too much. They will come and go, rise and fall, grow and die. What endures is the mission of God. God calls your church to mission.

—Kennon L. Callahan

NOTES

STUDY 12

SOLID FINANCIAL RESOURCES

Righteous God: you have taught us that the poor shall have your kingdom, and that the gentle-minded shall inherit the earth. Keep the church poor enough to preach to poor people, and humble enough to walk with the despised. Never weigh us down with real estate or too much cash on hand. Save your church from vain display or lavish comforts, so that, traveling light, we may move through the world showing your generous love, made known in Jesus Christ our Lord. Amen.

—Prayer for the Offertory

INTRODUCING "SOLID FINANCIAL RESOURCES"

It may be a surprise to discover that this key is twelfth in order of priority, and not first or second. We need to learn this lesson. Many congregations, when they discover their financial resources are reducing, usually wonder how they can increase the giving through a fund-raising campaign. This chapter reminds us of a number of important principles which are critical for us to recognize.

Logically, there are only two ways to increase the giving of a congregation. The first is to ask those who are already giving to give more (the usual approach). The other way is to have more people who want to give.

Read carefully the section on page 111: *Money follows mission,* and on page 112: *People give to people.* It may save us from some bad mistakes.

There are some technical matters in this chapter. You may invite a financially literate member of the group to help with these, or better yet, you can attend to the principles and leave the financial technicalities for the planning stage.

LOOKING AT THE BIBLE

MATTHEW 6:31–33

So do not worry, saying, "What shall we eat?" or "What shall we drink?" or "What shall we wear?" For the pagans run after all these things and your heavenly Father knows that you need them. But seek first his kingdom and his righteousness, and all these things will be given to you as well.

This passage is another portion of the teaching of Jesus in the Sermon on the Mount. The emphasis here is on the absolute priority of seeking the Kingdom of God and his righteousness. This applies equally to Christian congregations and to individuals.

Verse 31: **Do not worry.** Worry is a consequence of doubt. It is essentially a distrust of God.

Verse 32: **For the pagans run after all these things.** Anxiety is pagan, i.e., a heathen attitude. Christians believe in the love of God, and therefore the personal care of God for them.

Verse 33: **Seek first his Kingdom.** This means to give first priority to God in our own lives, the life of our church, and the life of the world.

. . . and his righteousness—means that while we may live imperfectly, God's righteousness will hold us steady. The message of the gospel is not that we can be righteous by ourselves, but that we are loved. The more we allow ourselves to be loved, the more possibility we have of living lives in God's grace, peace, and righteousness. The *righteousness* is God's, not ours.

. . . and all these things will be given to you. A clear example of Jesus' teaching that *money follows mission.* When we get mission right as a congregation through compassion and hope, we should not have to be so concerned about money.

Does the church have any responsibility to fulfill this focus of Jesus in its own congregational and institutional life?

UNLOCKING THE TWELFTH KEY

1. It would be helpful to ask a member of the group to turn to the first key and read to the group the section on pages 8 and 9 of *Twelve Keys to an Effective Church* entitled *Living Legends of Help.*

    How does this section resonate with the thoughts in this chapter?

2. We all learn various values and feelings about money.

    Share your own sense of the place and role of money in your own life.

3. In the section entitled *Development of Resources* (pages 111–15), five principles are discussed.

    Which of these does your congregation have well in place? Which of these can you advance and improve during the coming four years?

Help people see that their giving to the church is an investment, not a tax. Help them to see that they are investing in people's lives and destinies.

—Kennon L. Callahan

NOTES

THE PLANNING STEP

DEVELOPING A LONG-RANGE PLAN

Having completed the Study, the Long-Range Plan (three to five years) is developed by as many members of the congregation as is possible. This larger group is called "Congregation Long-Range Planning Committee."

The Planning step is undertaken by using the *Twelve Keys Planning Workbook*. It involves four stages to be completed in six sessions. It is crucial that everyone in the Planning step be familiar with the primary resource *Twelve Keys to an Effective Church*. The *Twelve Keys Planning Workbook* makes best sense when this is the case.

The steering committee can arrange the place, time, and leadership of the six sessions.

Parishes with More Than One Congregation

If the parish has more than one congregation there will need to be a decision whether all the congregations are to be involved in Planning or only some.

It is a reasonable decision, if thought appropriate, for a different congregation to commence the Planning process in each successive year.

It is also reasonable for a parish to decide that all the congregations will be invited to do the Study and Planning together. If this procedure is followed, it is most helpful for each congregation eventually to prepare its own plan.

Optional Procedures for Six Planning Sessions

Each person in the Congregation Long-Range Planning Committee should be given a *Twelve Keys Planning Workbook*. When the process is complete each person will have a detailed copy, in their own handwriting, of the Long-Range Plan for their **own** congregation. The Workbook procedure enables everyone present to contribute towards the formulation of the congregational plan. *The Leaders' Guide* is an invaluable resource in helping the Congregation Long-Range Planning Committee to accomplish its work effectively.

The Planning step is best accomplished in as short a time as possible. The purpose of planning is action, not planning. Some possibilities for the six planning sessions are:

1. a weekend Planning retreat

2. two Saturdays, involving three sessions each

3. two sessions in your local situation, and a weekend retreat involving four sessions

4. six sessions, one each week on a consecutive basis

5. six sessions, one every other week on a consecutive basis

You will know of other possibilities. Thousands of churches have benefited from these Planning sessions.

Report the Plan to the Congregation

Include the names of those recommended to put the plan into action.

The congregation should consider having a Service of Celebration to recognize the Plan as God's gift, and to help the congregation rejoice at the opportunity it offers for a new way ahead.

Publish the Plan

Have the plan published in a booklet, so the congregation can see clearly what we are being called to accomplish in the coming three to five years. Include a prayer to be used by the congregation for the year ahead. Share the booklet with persons in the community, with visitors, and with new members.

THE ACTION STEP

Action is the third step. Now that the Planning step has been completed it is important that the steering committee encourage progress in implementing the congregation's planned objectives for the coming twelve months.

It is strongly recommended that the steering committee undertake a further study of *The Twelve Keys Leaders' Guide*, focussing particularly on Part 2, *Resources for Action, Implementation, and Momentum* (pages 67–103).

Each meeting of the board or council can reflect on what is happening to achieve the key objectives of the long-range plan, and consider ways they may assist.

Twelve-Monthly Review

This is an opportunity for the congregation as a whole to review the Mission Plan. The following agenda is helpful:

A. LOOKING BACK

The original goals and objectives for Year I can be reviewed, and progress (or lack thereof) acknowledged. Remember, a great deal can be learned from "excellent mistakes." Not all objectives may have been realized.

B. LOOKING FORWARD

Now the reflections on Year I should be brought to bear on the original plans for Year II. Now is the time to make adjustments. Delete some objectives. Modify some objectives. Advance and improve some objectives.

C. LONG-TERM PLANNING

Whether the original Long-Range Plan was for three or five years, it is now time to add the new third or new fifth year to the original plan. Always be looking at least three years ahead.

The steering committee and as many of the members of the Church as possible can develop the key objectives for the new third year. New people who have joined the congregation can be invited to study *Twelve Keys* and join in the Planning meeting. In so doing, the Planning is kept dynamic. Remember, *Planning and Prayer go together.*

ENCOURAGEMENT ACTIVITIES

Suggest the congregation give your Study——Plan——Action for the coming three to five years a special name, e.g., *Towards 2000, Vision 2000, Forward Together, Mission and Hope.*

- Have a poster made listing the twelve keys for the congregation. Highlight the ones on which you are focusing.

- Helpful brief quotations of a sentence or two from the *Twelve Keys* books, properly credited, may be printed in your weekly newsletter or worship bulletin, e.g., "The purpose of planning is action, not planning."

- Christian witness during worship: a member of the Study group or steering committee could be interviewed or invited to witness to a recent exciting discovery.

- Invite several persons to make banners which symbolize the central characteristics on which you are focusing.

- Set up a prayer calendar to support the persons who are helping to accomplish your long-range mission plan.

- Create a spirit of compassion and a sense of hope in your own life and in the life of your congregation.

Hope is stronger than memory.
Memory is strong.
Hope is stronger.

We are the Easter People.
We are the People of Hope.

God bless you. God be with you.
—Kennon L. Callahan

Kennon L. Callahan, Ph.D., is the most sought-after consultant with churches of all denominations. He is highly respected for his wisdom, insights, experience, and research. He is a gifted lecturer and seminar leader, known for the wisdom, humor, and dynamic of his presentations.

Dr. Callahan's most recent book is *Effective Church Leadership.* In addition, he has written the best-selling *Twelve Keys to an Effective Church,* its *Leaders' Guide,* the *Planning Workbook,* and the *Twelve Keys* audiocassettes. *The Twelve Keys Study Guide* is his sixth publication.

Dr. Callahan's two new books, part of the series building on the Twelve Keys, are *Giving and Stewardship in an Effective Church* and *Effective Church Finances.*

Ian B. Tanner is among the significant leaders of the church in Australia and around the world. He has served on many national and international bodies to advance the mission of the Church.

He is past President of the Assembly of The Uniting Church in Australia, the union of the Congregational, Methodist, and Presbyterian denominations. A gifted preacher and teacher, much appreciated for his insights, wit, and thoughtfulness, for many years he was the senior pastor of the leading church in Adelaide, South Australia.

Presently, he serves as Director of Uniting Vision and is known for his remarkable leadership in strengthening the mission of local congregations in Australia.